SPEEDY MACHINES
CARS

Staplehurst Library
(01580 891929)

3 0 MAR 2012

2 5 MAY 2012

6 NOV 2010

2 6 FEB 2011

WITHDRAWN

2 9 OCT 2011

- 1 DEC 2011

1 4 FEB 2012

18/09/18

- 8 MAR 2012

Books should be returned or renewed by the
last date stamped above

Awarded for excellence
to Arts & Libraries

Kent
County
Council
EDUCATION & LIBRARIES

KT-173-481

Vic Parker
Illustrated by Tom Connell

C151407146

KENT
ARTS & LIBRARIES

C151407146

First published in the UK in 1999 by
Belitha Press Limited
London House, Great Eastern Wharf
Parkgate Road, London SW11 4NQ

This paperback edition first published in 1999

Copyright © Belitha Press Ltd 1999
Text copyright © Vic Parker 1999

All rights reserved. No part of this book may be reproduced or utilized in any form or
by any means, electronic or mechanical, including photocopying, recording or by any
information storage and retrieval system, without permission in writing from the
publisher except by a reviewer who may quote brief passages in a review.

ISBN 1 84138 132 2 (paperback)
ISBN 1 84138 010 5 (hardback)
ISBN 1 84138 128 4 (big book)

British Library Cataloguing in Publication Data
for this book is available from the British Library.

Printed in Singapore

Editor: Stephanie Bellwood
Designer: Helen James
Illustrator: Tom Connell
Consultant: Margaret Bellwood

Contents

Car power

Have you ever travelled in a fast car? The world outside whizzes past in a blur. Fast cars come in all shapes and sizes. There are large, stylish supercars and small, speedy sports cars. There are long, low racing cars and rough, tough rally cars. This book tells you all about these exciting machines.

The **engine** is usually at the front of the car. It is covered by the **bonnet**.

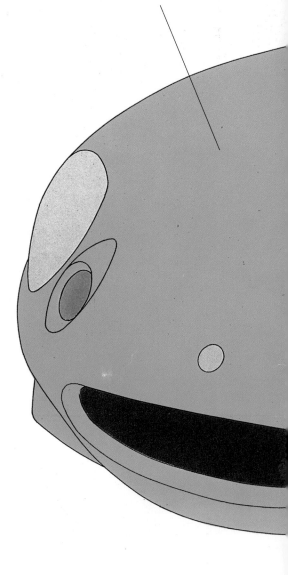

4

The driver's window is called the **windscreen**.

Turning the **steering wheel** changes the car's direction.

Some fast cars have a strip of metal on the back called a **spoiler**. It is shaped to help the car move faster.

Thick rubber **tyres** help the car grip the road.

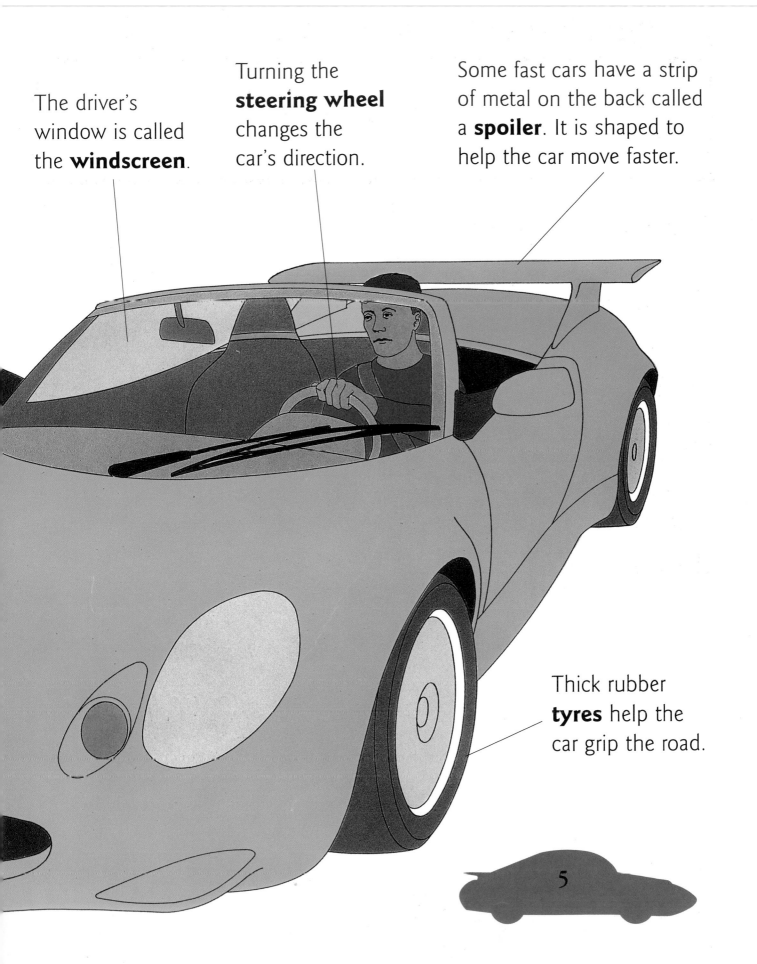

5

Track stars

These Formula One cars are racing each other in the famous Grand Prix championship. The cars fight to overtake each other as they swerve round corners. The drivers work hard to keep their speed machines under control. If they make a mistake they might spin dangerously off the track.

Fast facts

Racing cars zoom along at more than 300 km/h. The speed of a Formula One car is controlled by an on-board computer.

Formula One race

Built for speed

Porsche *Boxster*

A fast car has to be specially designed. It needs a powerful engine and a light, strong body. A low, smooth shape helps it move swiftly through the air. Ideas for new cars are tried out on computer. This Porsche *Boxster* is designed to roar along at 240 km/h.

Fast facts

Racing cars are made of a tough material that has air trapped inside. This makes the cars extra light and fast.

Speed testing

Engineers test a new car design to make sure that it works properly. A car is placed in a wind tunnel and coloured smoke is blasted around it at high speeds. If the air flows smoothly over the car designers know that it is properly shaped. The car is then crashed into a wall to check how strong and safe it is.

Fast facts

This McLaren *F1* is one of the world's fastest road cars. It has unusual doors that lift upwards instead of opening outwards. They are called gull-wing doors.

McLaren *F1* in wind tunnel

Racing machines

Indy car

This American Indy car is so speedy that it risks slipping out of control. Its heavy engine is at the back to press the car down on the ground. Extra wide rubber tyres help the car grip the track. The racing car is so long and low that the driver has to lie down to fit inside.

Fast facts

A racing car often needs new tyres during a race. It pulls into a pit stop and a motor racing crew leaps into action. The crew can change all four tyres in under ten seconds and then the car zooms away to join the race again.

Dragsters

The fastest racing cars are dragsters. They are the noisiest too! Dragsters race in pairs and shoot down a straight track longer than three football pitches. The race is over quickly because the cars reach speeds of more than 490 km/h. You can feel the ground shake as they thunder down the drag strip.

Fast facts

Many dragster drivers build their own speed machines using ordinary trucks, vans or cars and adding huge engines and wheels. These strange-looking cars are called Funny cars.

dragster

Difficult driving

Rallies are long-distance races over country roads and tracks. Rally cars are specially built to cope with tough, dangerous conditions such as deserts, muddy hills and icy roads. Staying in control of the car is more important than going very fast.

rally car

Fast facts

A rally car has a crew of two people. The driver controls the car. The navigator reads a map and shouts out instructions.

Supercar style

The biggest, fastest cars made for driving on roads are called supercars. They look smart and elegant outside. Inside they are very comfortable. Supercars cost a lot of money because they are fitted with the best engines, brakes and controls. This Ferrari 550 is one of the most expensive supercars.

Ferrari 550

Fast facts

Many supercars have their engine at the back instead of under the bonnet. This helps the back wheels to grip the road better.

King of the road

This Jaguar *XJ220* is a road car but it can move just as fast as a Formula One racing car. Its top speed is an amazing 350 km/h! Every part of this long, wide car is shaped so that it can go fast. Even the wing mirrors and door handles are specially shaped.

Fast facts

The Ferrari *F50* is one of the world's fastest supercars. It can start moving and speed up to 100 km/h in four seconds.

Jaguar *XJ220*

Engine power

The biggest, heaviest cars in the world are made in America. Huge machines such as the Dodge *Viper* are nicknamed gas guzzlers because they use up lots of petrol. Chevrolets are called muscle cars because their engines are so powerful. This Chevrolet *Corvette* can reach a speed of 97 km/h in less than five seconds.

Chevrolet *Corvette*

Fast facts

The most powerful engines of all are rocket engines. A few rocket cars have been built, but they are difficult to control and very dangerous.

Fast fun

Renault *Spider*

Cars don't have to be big to go fast. Sports cars zip around at top speeds because they are so small and light. Sports cars are made for fun! They aren't designed to carry passengers or luggage. It's very exciting to ride in an open-topped sports car like this Renault *Spider*. You can feel the wind rush past as you whizz along.

Fast facts

Some sports cars have headlights that pop up from the bonnet. They fold away afterwards so they don't spoil the car's smooth shape.

Super sports cars

This Lotus *Elise* is one of the speediest sports cars. It can move from standing still to 100 km/h in just six seconds. The *Elise* is made from a light metal called aluminium. This makes it half the weight of many other sports cars.

Fast facts

New sports cars are faster than ever. The Porsche *911 Carrera S* can race along at a fantastic 270 km/h.

Lotus *Elise*

Record breakers

The fastest car in the world is *Thrust SSC*. In 1997 it travelled at an incredible 1,227 km/h and set a new land speed record. Other people are trying to build even faster machines to beat the record. This car is called *Spirit of America*. It looks and travels just like a bullet!

Fast facts

Thrust SSC is driven by two enormous jet engines. These make the car as powerful as 141 Formula One racing cars.

Spirit of America

Facing the future

What type of car will you drive in the future? You might choose a stunning sports supercar like this daring new design. Perhaps you'll pick a car that doesn't use petrol. It might run on an electric battery or take its power from the sun. Maybe you won't drive at all. Your car might have a computer that does the driving for you!

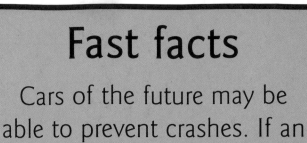

Fast facts

Cars of the future may be able to prevent crashes. If an object or another car is too close, the car will detect it and brake automatically.

Venus car design

Index